D0031853

International Foundation Mozarteum

Mozart Memorials in Salzburg

with a
Catalogue of objects displayed
in Mozart's birthplace

Edited by the International Foundation Mozarteum
Printing: Salzburger Druckerei

Wood Carving
by Leonhard Posch (May 1789)
Original in the Mozart Museum, Salzburg

TABLE OF CONTENTS

Visiting Hours:

Mozarteum and Magic Flute Cottage: Guided tours with organ performance 11.30 in July and August on weekdays

Mozart Museum: daily 9 a. m. — 6 p. m.,
June and September: 9 a. m. — 7 p. m., July and August:
8 a. m — 8 p. m. Mozart's residential house: From the end
of June to the beginning of September: 5 p. m. chamber
music concerts.

The Mozarteum on Schwarzstraße

The International Foundation
Mozarteum

"Dommusikverein (Society for Church Music) and Mozarteum" were founded in April 1841, their task being to revive music of all kinds, but especially church music. The Society was not very successful in their endeavours, and only after the "Society for Church Music and Mozarteum" had been changed into the "International Foundation", newly founded in 1870, did remarkable financial means make it possible to begin effective work. The activity of the Foundation was very successful and soon increased to such an extent that it was thought necessary to separate the Dommusikverein from the Mozarteum, and to add a music school to the latter. But only 10 years later the separation could be accomplished. In 1880 the "Dommusik-verein and Mozarteum" changed their name and have since been called "The International Foundation Mozarteum". There is a General Meeting once a year, "Mozart Day", when the members elect a board of administration to see to the duties of the Foundation. In the autumn of 1880 the Foundation opened a music school in the so-called "Anatomiestöckl" of the university, opposite the present Festival House. A small marble tablet on the building in the Hofstallgasse still reminds us of that event.

The Music School became renowned during the following years and was made a conservatory in 1914. The International Foundation Mozarteum then gave the Music School a worthy and convenient place for its activity in the newly-built Mozarteum. In 1922 the state took over the administration of the Music School as the Foundation had suffered severe losses by the devaluation of the currency and could no longer meet its expenses. The International Foundation Mozarteum provided rooms to the Music University and placed instruments and a library at its disposal. It also took care of the Mozart Museum in the house where Mozart was born, bougth the house in 1917 and the house, where he lived from 1773 to 1780, in 1955.

By organizing concerts (since 1881) and later on by opening a booking-office for concerts and plays (in 1924), the Foundation exercised great influence on the musical interests of Salzburg. From time to time Musical Festivals were arranged which gradually developed into the now world-famous "Salzburg Festivals".

By establishing the "Bibliotheca Mozartiana" (1912), by arranging sessions for music and exhibitions, and by founding a Central Institute for Mozart Research (1931) which issues a Mozart Almanac every year, the International Foundation Mozarteum tried to make the Salzburg Mozarteum the centre for Mozart Research in all the world.

Since 1933 the International Foundation Mozarteum arranged everey year during the summer months music classes for training conductors and other musicians, called the "Salzburg Academy", which had to interrupt its work during the war and was then taken over by the Music University.

The "Mozart Medal" is given as a distinction to persons of special merit, and the "Lilli Lehmann Medal" to pupils who excel in their studies and play.

Mozart Medal

In 1888 the "Mozartgemeinde" was founded, which assists the International Foundation Mozarteum in its work. It has branches all over the world that connect those who are active in cultivating and propagating Mozart's music. Without their help it would have been impossible to build the Mozarteum, to buy the house in which Mozart was born, the numerous manuscripts, music autographs, original pictures and other objects.

Since 1877 the foundation has taken care of the "Zauberflötenhäuschen" (the little wooden house in which Mozart composed the opera "The Magic Flute") which has been removed from the Kapuzinerberg and set up in 1952 in the garden behind the Mozarteum.

There are still many tasks to be accomplished by the International Foundation and the Mozartgemeinde: so a complete new edition of Mozart's works as a monument to commemorate the 200th anniversary of his birthday in cooperation with the Central Institute for Mozart Research in Salzburg. The whole edition will include 110 volumes of music and will be finished 1980 with the help of the committees which have already been formed in many countries: namely the organization called "Pro Mozart". Subscriptions can be sent to the International Foundation Mozarteum.

The Mozart Monument

Recognition of the importance of W. A. Mozart came only after the death of the great master. In Salzburg, veneration of Mozart began early in the nineteenth century. At this time Morzart's widow Constance, then Staatsraetin von Nissen, still lived in Salzburg. His sister Nannerl, widow of Reichsfreiherr von Berchtold, was also spending her last years there. Constanze's second husband, the Danish councillor Georg Nikolaus von Nissen, had published a comprehensive biography of Mozart after many years of preparation. Mozart admirers from all over the world visited the Nissens to learn more about the great composer and to visit the places where he had lived and worked, especially the birthplace.

When the composer was but fifteen years old, however, the Mozart family moved from the Getreidegasse to the more friendly atmosphere of Hannibalplatz and scarcely any relics were left at the birthplace to remind posterity of Salzburg's most famous son.

Only in 1835 a monument was contemplated. For this purpose appeals were launched, concerts and theatrical performances were given and large sums were raised.

Mozart Monument in Mozart Square

When the civic authorities had their plans complete, Mozart's widow surprised them with the suggestion that the money would be better spent on a music school. She also suggested that her son, Wolfgang Amadeus, be appointed as its director.

As this proposal found no support and since, in the meantime, Constanze died, the design of the Munich sculptor Ludwig von Schwanthaler was finally executed in 1841. However the monument was not erected until the following year, because the necessary excavations revealed extensive Roman mosaik floors, which had to be removed carefully. In September, 1842, the bronze statue, cast in Munich, was brought to Salzburg and set up with great ceremony on the occasion of the first Musical Festival.

„Wiener Saal" in the Mozarteum

11

Middle piece of the organ case in the "Wiener Saal"

The Mozarteum Building

The Mozarteum building is situated near the river Salzach, close to the old fortifications and the Mirabell gardens. It was erected during the years 1910 to 1914 according to the prizewinning design of the Munich architect Richard Berndl.

In the middle of the nineteenth century a number of

enthusiastic citizens of Salzburg were inspired to create a permanent institution in commemoration of the great composer Mozart. A fund was started to which Mozart-lovers of the whole world subscribed. Foremost in the ranks of these enthusiasts were Gregor Baldi, founder of the fund, and Friedrich Gehmacher, president of the Mozartgemeinde.

The building itself comprises a school for music and a concert-hall. The richly decorated façade of the school-building is modelled after the late Baroque style, while the concert-hall façade with its projecting entrance hall, suggests the severer trends of the classical era.

Two bronze figures, larger than life-size, and representing the cheerful and the serious music, by the sculptor Georg Römer, are on the façade of the school-building. The gable is surmounted by four cherubs, symbolic of the musical tempi allegro, andante, alla marcia and menuetto. These were the work of the Munich sculptor Karl Killer. In the hall of the school-building are marble tablets commemorating the founders. This building contains the classrooms and offices and is the headquarters of the Salzburg Choral Society (Salzburger Liedertafel). The president's office, secretary's office, the library of the Foundation (Stiftung) and the small concert-hall are also situated here.

In 1940 it was necessary to enlarge the school-building. This work was undertaken by the architect Dr. Hans Hofmann of Salzburg and the building was extended on the side of the Mirabell gardens. This new wing contains the school library, rehearsal rooms and classrooms. The upper floor is decorated with portraits of President Freiherr von Hilleprandt, Graf Kuenburg, Hofrat Gehmacher, the great benefactress and opera singer Lilli Lehmann and the first Director of the Music-school Josef Friedrich Hummel, the lower floor with that of Bernhard Paumgartner. The library of the International Foundation Mozarteum is the pivot around which all Mozart study and research revolve.

On its shelves are the complete works of Mozart, published by the Foundation in 1875, the complete works of Bach, **Palestrina, Händel, Beethoven** and **Schubert.** The works of other German and Austrian composers are also there. Adjoining the library ist the secretary's office, which houses the most treasured of all Mozart's bequests, his manuscripts.

Ceiling relief in the "Wiener Saal"

For smaller concerts, there is the Wiener Saal, so-called because it was provided by funds donated by the Mozart Society of Vienna (Wiener Mozartgemeinde). In this hall there is an organ with thirty six stops and two manuals. On the ceiling is a noteworthy relief "Apollo in the sun chariot" (Apollo im Sonnenwagen), the work of Konrad Buchner.

The other part of the building contains the large concert-hall. In the foyer stands a life-size bronze statue by the Viennese sculptor Edmund v. Helmer, representing Mozart as Apollo Musagetes. Before its base is the foundation stone, which was laid on August 6th, 1910. The concert-hall is reached by staircases and corridors, the walls of which are hung with pictures by Niemeyer, Klemm, Diez and a relief by Moos. It is generally accepted that the atmosphere of the concert-hall is such that it seems to create a bond between performer and listener. The proportions and decorations of the hall contribute to this pleasing atmosphere. The excellent acoustic effects are brought about by the ingenions building construction. The Arco-organ with its four manuals and fifty seven stops was built by the well known firm of W. Walcker and finished in 1970 by a donation of Gertrud Countess Arco-Valley.

There is a buffet between the concert-hall and the school-building and this leads to the old bastion with the Magic Flute cottage, from which can be seen the old openair theater, the Mirabell gardens and Schloß Mirabell.

Since the opening of the concert-hall many artists from all over the world have commented upon its excellent features and the serene spirit which pervades it, giving pleasure to performer and listener alike.

Large concert-hall in the Mozarteum

Library in the Mozarteum

The Mozart Archives

The Mozart Archives were set 1841, at the same time as the "Dommusikverein und Mozarteum". Out of the latter emerged in 1880 the "Internationale Stiftung Mozarteum".

Donations and the legacy of Mozart's son Carl formed the basis of the archives. Manuscripts were added through the decades.

Every year during Festival Season there is an exhibition in the rooms of the library, comprising the most interesting letters and manuscripts of the master and his friends, as well as letters of his family. Combined, they give us a close-up view of Mozart's life and work.

The first five letters are by Leopold Mozart to his wife. They were written during the first Italian trip in 1769 and bear postscripts of the thirteen-year-old Wolfgang. Through them we get an idea of the young composer's unparalleled triumphs in Italy. Their route took father and son through Milan, Bologna, Rome and Naples. In Rome the knighthood of the "Order of the Golden Spur", a distinction that carried with it the title of nobility, was bestowed on Wolfgang by Pope Clemens XIV for writing down from memory Allegri's famous Miserere which he had heard in the Sistine Chapel.

In Naples Wolfgang gave a concert in the Conservatorio della Pieta and the superstitious Neapolitans believed that the astonishing technique of his left hand was due to his ring, a present of the Empress Maria Theresia.

In Bologna he was unanimously elected a member of the "Accademia Filarmonica", certainly the greatest recognition of his unique talent. There he worked on his opera "Mitridate", which was first performed in Milan in 1770. It was Mozart's first theatrical success: the opera was performed twenty times before a full house.

After their return to Salzburg in March 1771 Wolfgang was commissioned by the Viennese Court to write a theatrical serenade for the wedding of Archduke Ferdinand in Milan in October. This was reason enough for another trip to Italy. In August he left Salzburg, and in twelve days he had completed the score of the serenade "Ascanio in Alba", which was performed under his direction on October 17th.

At the age of sixteen Wolfgang went to Italy for the third and last time in order to prepare the performance of his latest opera "Lucio Silla" in Milan. Again, it was a success.

However, further opera commissions for Italy did not materialize. Leopold was disappointed in the hope of obtaining for Wolfgang a secure position with the Archduke of Tuscany in Florence. Thus, the following year, both of them returned into the services of the Archbishop of Salzburg.

When in July 1773 they went to Vienna, father Leopold once more hoped for a well-paid position for his son at the court of the Empress Maria Theresia, for Wolfgang had been commissioned to write a serenade for the wedding of Archduke Ferdinand. Unfortunately nothing came of it. Bitterly disappointed, Leopold Mozart wrote home: "The Empress received us very graciously, but that was all."

The following period in Salzburg was one of the most productive of Wolfgang's life; one year saw the birth of several symphonies and a great deal of church music.

Kurfuerst Maximilian of Bavaria commissioned Mozart to write an opera for the Carnival of 1775. Wolfgang himself directed the performance in the Bavarian capital. "Thank God, my opera came off last night. It was so good, that I cannot possibly describe to you, dear mother, the noise of the applause", he reports.

In the three quiet years that followed he composed almost 100 works. Meanwhile, father Leopold used this time to try and secure by correspondence the coveted position abroad. In the spring of 1777 he approached the archbishop with the request to grant him and his son a leave of several months. The Archbishop refused, saying that he did not want his musicians to be vagrant beggars, whereupon young Mozart tendered his resignation. This document contains the sentence: ". . . the more talents children have received from God, the more they are bound to use them — this we are taught in the Gospels." Quick-witted the Archbishop answered this resignation, whose author he easily recognized as father Mozart, with the remark: ". . . father and son, according to the Gospels, have the permission to seek for their luck elsewhere..." The family Mozart had not been prepared for such an answer. Though the dismissal of father Mozart was cancelled later, Wolfgang had found the longed—for freedom. In September he started on the great journey that was to take him as far as Paris; in his father's stead his mother, who was then 57 years of age, accompanied him. Again his father strongly advised him to look out for a position at a European court. But once more Wolfgang found that empty words and promises were all that materialized from brilliant receptions and celebrations.

From Munich he wrote home that many good friends would like him to remain there, but they had no influence, and the Kurfuerst himself thought it too early and had advised him to make his name in Italy first. Augsburg, father Leopold's birthplace, was the next station. In two concerts he presented himself to the Augsburgers. His recital was greatly admired, but he suffered from the bad accompaniment of the local orchestra.

After several other stays in small German cities, he reached Mannheim which was then a centre of arts and sciences. Of its orchestra members some were famous musicians. With Christian Cannabich, the conductor, he was soon bound in friendship. The Kurfuerst became interested and began talking about piano lessons for his children. But in December of this year he had to report home "this time nothing came of it . . ." His hopes for a later chance disappeared when the Kurfuerst left Mannheim for Munich to take over the government there on the death of Maximilian. The artists followed and Mannheim became deserted.

From the Mannheim period there are about 26 letters in the archive, four of them on exhibition. One of them is a congratulation on his father's anniversary, dated November 8th, 1777. It begins: "My very dearest papa! I cannot write poetically; I am no poet; I cannot arrange the sentences so artfully that they give light and shade;

I am no painter. I cannot even express my thoughts and feelings by gestures and pantomimes; I am no dancer, but I can do it through tones, I am a musician . . ."

The following letter is the only preserved and authentic one in Mozart literature in which young Mozart added his title to his signature and included a gay joke. He signed himself: "Wolfgang Amadé Mozart Knight of the Golden Spur (des Goldenen Sporns), and as soon as I am married, I am cuckolded (des doppelten Horns), Member of the great Academy of Verona, Bologna, oui mon ami!"

Father Leopold could not understand why his son, in spite of the hopelessness of finding a position at the court, did not proceed to Paris, but remained in Mannheim. Finally Wolfgang explained to his father: he had met a Mr. Weber whose daughter Aloisia had such a wonderful voice that she only needed action to make her a prima donna. He suggested that he would go to Italy with them.

This news was a blow to Leopold. He immediately wrote a stern, long letter to his son to get him back on the right road. He told him to give up these foolish plans worthy only of a vagrant, and to proceed to Paris immediately: "From Paris the fame and name of a man goes through the world."

Now there was no more hesitation. Inwardly still revolting, Wolfgang had to follow his father's strict orders. As he left Mannheim, Aloisia swore eternal love.

The Paris of 1778 was torn between the followers of the national opera and those of Italian music. In this confusion we find Mozart trying to stimulate interest in his work. Again he is admitted to the houses of high nobility, again he hears beautiful words, but he does not even succeed in getting the organist's position at Versailles. With bitter feelings he makes his plans for leaving the city. There, on July 3rd, 1778, he receives the heaviest blow: death takes away his beloved mother. All of a sudden he stands alone, far from home. He writes to his friend Abbé Bullinger in Salzburg, to prepare his family. A few days later he gives a detailed account to his father of his mother's illness and death.

On his way back from Paris he came to Munich where Aloisia had meanwhile become an opera star who had but a sympathetic smile for the poor musician. His heart filled with bitter disappointment, he finally arrived in Salzburg, lovingly received by his father, his sister and old friends.

In the period of quiet work that now followed, he composed symphonies, serenades and, among other church music, the famous "Krönungsmesse".

In the fall of 1780 Kurfürst Karl Theodor commissioned Mozart to write an opera for the Carnival of 1781. "Idomeneo" was created and successfully performed. In the middle of the gaiety in Munich, Archbishop Colloredo ordered him to come to Vienna immediately. Empress Maria Theresia had died and the archbishop had moved to the capital with his court. He did not want to miss his star-artist.

Mozart followed the order with a glad heart. He hoped to renew his relationship with the imperial court and nobility. But the Archbishop did not permit him to give concerts. Still he succeeded in coming in contact with

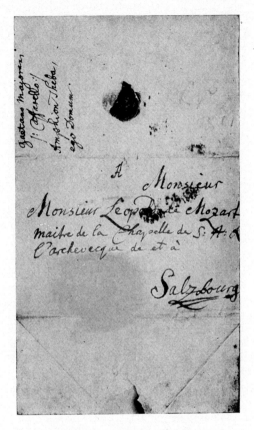

Envelope from Mozart to his father

the musical world there, and the encouragement he received everywhere confirmed his opinion that he had found Vienna „as the place in the world for a man of his profession". He already visualized himself as a renowned and celebrated artist, when the archbishop's order that he should go back to Salzburg immediately woke him rudely from his hopeful dreams. Mozart hesitated to fulfil this order. The Archbishop called him in; the audience ended in a dispute, whereupon Mozart resigned from his services.

At last he was rid of the fetters and free to live for his art and work alone. It was a freedom dearly bought.

The successful performances of his opera "The Abduction from the Seraglio" (Vienna, July 16, 1782) seemed to give him the financial base to set up his own home, and in August 1782 he married Constanze Weber (sister of Aloisia), a step regarded as fatal by all biographers.

A period of luck und success followed. He found entry in the houses of nobility, had well paying pupils and made valuable connections. His economic situation was sound. The Mozarts kept an open house and gave with full hands to their many friends who knew how to flatter.

Gradually, however, disfavor, worries and want made their appearance. Mozart's concerts were less popular; the pupils became fewer; more and more often he had to request help from his friends. Had his wife known how to keep house, she might have averted complete ruin. But Constanze was without measure. If there was money in the house, it was spent. If there was not, there was the pawnshop. Debts were made from which Mozart could never free himself again.

Letters from this period testify to his precarious situation. When all sources had been tapped, he was forced to make compositions for some special occasion for ridiculous payment. The financial outcome neither of "Figaro" nor of "Don Giovanni" seemed to have helped much. His letters from the year 1788 show the steady downward trend of his finances.

A trip to Berlin and another to Frankfurt were intended to improve matters, but only brought new disappointments and showed clearly the hopelessness of the situation. Yet in this period he composed his greatest works, among

Page from the diary of Wolfgang and his sister Nannerl

Score of "La chasse"

others Titus, the Magic Flute, and his immortal swansong, the Requiem. The latter was never finished, for on December 5th, 1791, death took him in the midst of his work.

Mozart was buried in a pauper's grave. Poor also was his material legacy. His manuscripts, however, described as worthless at the time, were sold by his wife a few years afterwards for a very handsome sum.

A few friends remained faithful to him but none thought of visiting the last resting place of the unhappy master. And his dearly beloved wife Constanze? On her is the blame that the grave was forgotten and lost to posterity. Not until eighteen years later did she go to the cemetery and was shocked to find that no one could show her the site of the former pauper's grave: since nobody had taken an interest in it, it had been levelled down.

The exhibition closes with a few valuable manuscripts by Mozart's contemporaries such as Haydn's famous London Diary and the wellknown "Violinschule" by Leopold Mozart.

Part of a piano minuet for two hands
certified by Constanze

Mozart's Birthplace

Just where the narrow Getreidegasse opens into the Hagenauerplatz, we see a high old house facing the square, and a marble tablet informs us that this is the building in which Mozart was born. All those houses of the Middle Ages are narrow and deep, and the dark staircase and the rooms at the back of the house get their poor light from a small courtyard. The living-rooms are large and cosy, but the kitchen across the corridor with the old fashioned hearth and the floor paved with tiles, reminds us of the Middle Ages.

In 1585 the house was purchased by the chemist of the court, Chunrad Fröschlmoser, and we still see the emblems of Aesculap, the serpent in the lion's mouth, on the two wings of the front-door. The house changed ownership in 1703; the merchant Hagenauer who bought it and his son Lorenz became the landlords of the Mozart family. Leopold Mozart, violinist of the Archbishop, moved into the third floor in 1747, soon after his marriage. The flat consisted of the bed-room, in which his famous son was born, of a sitting-room, a study and a small room in which guests were received.

On January 27th, 1756, in the inner room looking out on the studded baroque tower of the University Church, Wolfgang Amadeus was born. In this house Mozart spent the first years of his life and most of his juvenile works, such as the first piano concerto, the Violin concertos and several symphonies were composed in its rooms.

In 1773 the family Mozart moved to the Hannibalplatz (now Makartplatz) near the theater.

For the centenary of Mozart's birthday an exhibition was arranged in the house where Mozart was born, and in 1880 the International Foundation Mozarteum adapted these rooms for a Mozart Museum. In the collection of pictures, autographs, documents and various relics, Mozart's "Hammerflügel", constructed by Anton Walter in Vienna, and his clavichord are the most precious things the museum can show.

In 1917 the International Foundation Mozarteum became the owner of the house and took care of restoring it in the old style. In 1931 some rooms on the second floor and, later on, some on the first floor were added for the display of objects, pictures, etc. about the history of the Mozart operas. You can follow the development of the scenery in the Mozart operas up to the present time by means of dioramas, sketches of sceneries and costumes.

a) The Mozart Museum

The "Dommusikverein and Mozarteum" received its first gifts in 1841 from Mozart's family. Constance and her sons, Karl and Wolfgang, donated several original portraits of the Master together with some manuscripts. These were exhibited in a modest little room in the Chiemseehof and were the beginning of the Mozart Museum. Later all the original portraits that had been in Constanze's possession were added to the museum. The museum itself was opened in 1880 in the Hagenauerplatz house.

The most precious treasure is the master's concert piano. Mozart had been particulary fond of this piano and used it in all his performances in his last ten years. His widow left it to their son Carl who later donated the piano to the museum.

A sister-instrument, built about 1800 by the same Viennese craftsman, was given to the International Foundation Mozarteum in 1937 and represents a valuable addition to the collection.

The clavichord was given to the Mozarteum by Constanze in her will. Pasted in it is a note in her own hand-writing: "On this instrument my husband Mozart composed, within five months the Magic-Flute, La Clemenza

Room where Mozart was born

Mozart's birthplace on Getreidegasse

di Tito, the Requiem and a new freemasons cantata. I, Mozart's widow and present wife of Councillor Nissen, confirm this."

Sweet memories are woven around the violin, on which Mozart played as a child, such as the one recounted by the Salzburg court trumpeter and violinist Andreas Schacht- ner. A friend of the Mozart family, he wrote to Wolf- gang's sister Nannerl: "Little Wolfgang asked to be allowed to play the second violin. But father told him this was nonsense, because he had never had any instruc- tions on it and would not be able to do anything with it . . . I pleaded to let him play, so in the end father said: 'All right, go on and play the violin with Mr. Schachtner, but so quietly that no one will hear you, or else you have to leave.' Soon I noticed with surprise that I was super- fluous. I put aside my violin and looked at your father whose face was wet with tears of admiration and relief." Among the earliest and most attractive of the many portraits are the one of six-year-old Wolfgang, the other of Nannerl in court dress on their first visite to the court of Maria Theresia. It gives a vivid impression of them, confirmed by Goethe in his remark to Eckermann: "I have seen him (Mozart) as a boy of seven. I was about 14 years old, and I remember very vividly the little man with his headdress and dagger."

The engraving of Delafosse, made after de Carmontelle's water color, depicts Mozart's father with his two children in Paris in 1764, just before their visit to the King of England. "The grace bestowed upon us by Their Majesties is indescribable", reports Leopold.

Among the famous pictures are "Mozart with the Golden Spur" (an award conferred upon him by Pope Clemens XIV) and another "Mozart with the Diamond Ring" (Maria Theresia's gift to the six-year-old child). Most valuable is de la Croce's family portrait showing Wolfgang and Nannerl at the piano, the father with his violin, and the kind face of the mother looking out from a painting on the wall. You will find this portrait now in the residence of the Mozart Family.

The only portrait of the mature Mozart is the unfinished oil painting by his brother-in-law, Josef Lange, from the Vienna period 1789. Together with Doris Stock's silver pencil drawing and Nissen's description, these are the only sources for reconstructing the outward appearance of the master: "His head was relatively big for his body, the body itself, hands and feet, well proportioned, of which he was a little proud. His nose was beautiful, only of striking size in the years when he was thin." The death mask crumbled in the hands of the widow, and the skull— quite apart from the scientific argument concerning its authenticity—can never transmit an impression of the living man Mozart. Therefore Lange's color portrait is of particular importance.

In the museum there is a display of coins and medals relating to the Master and the wood carving by Leonhard Posch (see page 3).

There are portraits of Mozart's parents, Leopold and Anna Maria, and of Constanze (in her later years); of her second husband Nissen (who is the autor of one of the first Mozart biographies), and of Mozart's sons Carl and Wolfgang. One pictures shows Nannerl as Baroness Berchtold zu Sonnenburg.

Glass showcases shrine the master's few personal belongings that are left to posterity: buttons from his court dress, his wallet, miniatures and decorations.

Among the treasures which are touching and impressive are Mozart's manuscripts, such as the little book of notes which father Leopold prepared for his daughter; his exercises in counterpoint; test composition and the award in the nature of a diploma by the Accademia Filarmonica of Bologna; further, a copy of Fux' "Gradus ad Parnassum". Last, not least, there is Leopold Mozart's "Versuch einer

33

Mozart in Court Dress from 1762

Unsigned oil-painting
Original in the Mozart Museum Salzburg

Mozart's sister Nannerl in Court Dress from 1762

Unsigned oil-painting
Original in the Mozart Museum Salzburg

gründlichen Violinschule" ("Essay on a complete Violin Course"). This work was first edited in Augsburg in 1756, the year of his great son's birth and became known far beyond the borders of his country.

It is a sad chapter in history that in the years of destruction, 1944 and 1945, a number of valuable possessions in the collection was lost. The hope is not unjustified that one day some of them will once more find their former place in the museum. The lost items are listed below. Any information which may help to locate them should be addressed to the "Internationale Stiftung Mozarteum", Salzburg.

Mozart's concert piano

The Mozart Family 1780/81
painted in oil by J. N. de la Croce in Salzburg
Original in the Residence of the Mozart Family in Salzburg

1. Mozart's golden watch, gift of Empress Maria Theresia. High old casing. Setting and indicators studdied with diamonds (c. 200). Back cover bearing portrait of Empress Maria Theresia. Inside engraving „W. A. Mozart 1786".

2. Golden Mozart Ring, with big agate and twelve diamonds.

3. Wax relief W. A. Mozart's by Leonhard Posch. Red relief on black ground, under glass. Reverse side containing handwritten dedication "The undersigned childhood friend of the father dedicated this to the son as a remembrance".

4. Meerschaum relief "Mozart on the belt-buckle". On glass background covered with blue velvet. Oval setting.

5. Album W. A. Mozart, red leather binding, 53 handwritten, partly illustrated pages with gilt edges. Entries from 1787 to 1830.

6. Album of Babette Ployer, same type as (4), containing funeral march composed by Mozart, water colors, pencil, sepia and chalk drawings, and a silhouette of Mozart with entry of widow Constanze.

7. Visiting card of Emanuel Schikaneder.

b) "Mozart in the Theater"

Rarely do we find a genius equal to Mozart's. Nothing testifies more clearly to his universal appeal than the many different forms of presentation of his dramatic work the world over. For this reason, a special exhibition was

Mozart, at the beginning of 1789
Unfinished oil-painting by Mozart's brother-in-law
Josef Lange in Vienna
Original in the Mozart Museum Salzburg

assembled in 1931 in the house where Mozart was born, showing the history of presentation of the Mozart opera through the age, with the "Magic Flute" as its centre.
A collection of nearly one hundred miniature stage models, movable and illuminated, gives an idea of the

Losses from the Mozart Museum

Wax relief W. A. Mozart's by Leonhard Posch
(See page 38, Nr. 3)

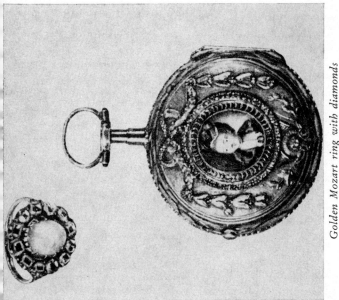

Golden Mozart ring with diamonds
(See page 38, Nr. 2)

Mozart's golden watch
(See page 38, Nr. 1)

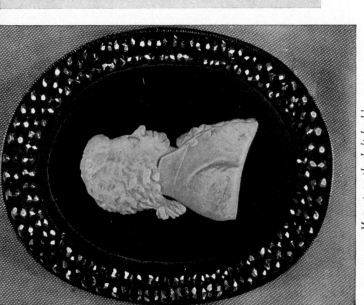

Mozart on the belt-buckle
(See page 38, Nr. 4)

changing interpretation of his work by succeeding generations. There we find the stages of Mozart's own period, the stages of the Biedermeier era, of the 19th century and of later epochs until the present day. Every nation has tried its hand at various solutions, the most interesting among them coming from Germany. Particulary "Don Giovanni" and "The Magic Flute" were the subject of continual study on the part of theater experts. But "The Marriage of Figaro", "Così Fan Tutte" and "The Abduction from the Seraglio" also present problems, different according to the respective development in stage technique, lighting, etc. In Mozart's dramatic work music and drama are deeply interwoven, so that the presentation as such is necessarily determined by the interpretation of the music, which is primary.

Thus the exhibition "Mozart in the Theater" is not only a joy to the eyes of the casual visitor, but also offers valuable inspiration, stimulus and opportunity for study to the theater expert and stage decorator. Last, not least, it is an avowel of Wolfgang Amadeus Mozart's immortal genius.

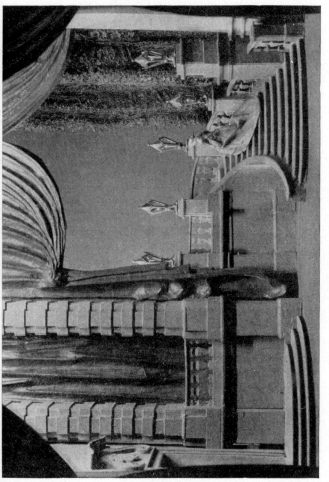

Scenery for "The Marriage of Figaro"

The Residence of the
Mozart Family

The birthplace of Mozart on the Hagenauerplatz gives
one a feeling of the narrowness of the medieval, walled
city. In contrast, the residence of the family represents a
"new" period that was more open to the world. This
house was the former "Tanzmeisterhaus am Hannibalplatz" (Dancing Master's House on Hannibal Square), the
Makartplatz today. Built at the beginning of the 17th century, outside the ancient town wall, it was in keeping with
the spirit of Fischer's von Erlach Trinity Church a few
steps away.

The house with its wide, windowed front faced the "Ball-
haus" which today is the Landestheater. Beyond, there
was an open view into the green Mirabell Gardens, — thus
indicating the longing of the period for space and light
and gaiety.

The young violinist Leopold Mozart may have made the
acquaintance of Dancing Master Spöckner at the Archbishop's court, and perhaps he took part in some of the
performances at the latter's house. It is certain that a
strong bond of friendship united the two men. Leopold
loved the light, spacious rooms, with their exquisitely
carved wooden ceiling. These early impressions, together
with those he received on his first Italian trip with his
son Wolfgang, emphasized more clearly the dark and
restricted character of the house on the Hagenauerplatz.
As early as February 1771 he wrote from Venice to his
wife: ". . . It has just occured to me that we cannot go on
living in our present home. Will you see if we could not
move somewhere else. We cannot continue to sleep like
soldiers. Wolfgang is no longer seven years old . . ."

MOZART'S WOHNHAUS

The residence of the Mozart family before destruction
Lithograph after G. Pezold, c. 1840

At Spöckner's death in the fall of 1773, Leopold rented Spöckner's house and moved his family into it.

There were eight high, almost ballroom-like rooms on the first floor. Wolfgang was seventeen years old at that time. The five and a half years of his life in the Tanzmeisterhaus were rich in musical creations. Here he composed divertimenti, the famous "Haffner" serenade, sonatas, symphonies, piano concertos and the "Krönungsmesse".

When the hopeful young Wolfgang and his mother left the house in September 1777, the good spirit of the house "am Hannibalgarten" seemed to disappear with them. Leopold writes of this departure: "I tried my best to hide my feelings when we said good-bye, so as not to make it harder for all of us, and in this confusion I forgot to give my son Wolfgang my paternal blessing. I ran to the window to send it after you both, but I did not see you leave through the door. We had to assume that you had already passed, for I had been sitting for some time dreaming."

In January 1779 Wolfgang returned alone to the Tanzmeisterhaus. Death had taken his dearly beloved mother in Paris on July 3, 1778. He himself had become a different person. His gay and childlike heart had received a deep wound in his unhappy love for Aloisia Weber. Again the burden of compulsory service at the Archbishop's court pressed heavily on his shoulders. In November 1780 he left the house forever. His visit in 1783 with his wife Constanze was that of a stranger. Too deeprooted was the mistrust of his father and sister against the Weber family.

When Mozart's sister Nannerl married and moved to St. Gilgen, the aging and sickly father Leopold lived in quietness in the Tanzmeisterhaus. A last ray of happiness came into his life when Nannerl's son Poldl was born in the Hannibalgarten house. On May 28, 1787, death came to Leopold.

The famous dancing master's ball after restitution 1956

Eight years later the printer Oberer acquired the house, and the noise of the printing presses filled the once lovely rooms.

As late as 1939 the Mozarteum School succeeded in renting the upper floor for its seminary and brought back to life some of the old spirit of the house. In 1944 this stately building became a victim of the war bombing. The rest of it with the famous music room of Leopold Mozart was purchased 1955 by the International Foundation Mozarteum, renovated 1956 in the correct style and made accessible to the public. So Salzburg is enriched by a new Mozart memorial.

The Magic Flute Cottage

(Das Zauberflöten-Häuschen)

Legends surround the birth of the Magic Flute. However the unpretentious wooden cottage, with its shingled roof, has gone into history as a concrete fact.

When Mozart began work on the Magic Flute in the spring of 1791, he was already fatally ill. As to whether the little house was a welcome retreat for him in his work, or whether the unscrupulous commissioner, librettist and director of the "Freihaustheater auf der Wieden", Emanuel Schikaneder, had intended to keep Mozart here under constraint, or whether it served as drinking and eating lodge to keep up the master's spirits and creative power, may remain a matter of legendary interpretation. It is certain, however, that in this cottage near the theater, right in the middle of the six open courtyards of the "Freihaus" in Vienna, the miracle of the Magic Flute was created in a bare five months.

Moreover, the little garden house symbolizes the personality of the genius Mozart and his own way of working. "Mozart's music does not need any outward stimulus; it is self-contained; it follows its own, heavenly laws, regardless of whether the sky of reality is clear or clouded" (A. Einstein "Mozart"). The inside of the weatherbeaten little cottage was once covered with silver wallpaper. It is the earthly shrine of Mozart's spiritual world as it is expressed in his last work, the Magic Flute. On September 30, 1791, the Magic Flute was performed for the first time. Nine weeks later Wolfgang Amadeus Mozart died at the age of 35 years and 10 months.

After Mozart's death, few people knew of the secret of the Zauberflötenhäuschen. We need not be surprised, therefore, to hear that at one time a poultry dealer used

The Magic Flute Cottage in the courtyard of the "Freihaus" in Vienna

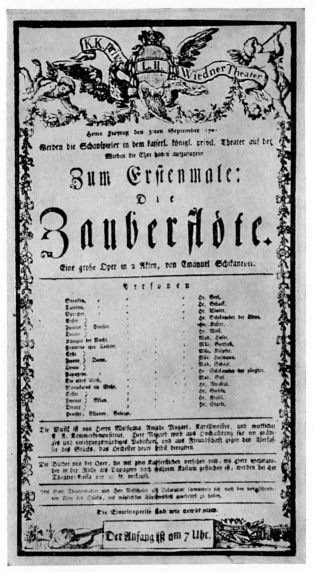

Theater bill for the first performance in the Freihaustheater
auf der Wieden on September 30, 1791

The Magic Flute Cottage in the Mozarteum Garden

it to house his rabbits. When in 1873 the "Freihaus" was offered for sale, the owner, Camillo Prince Starhemberg, planned to set up the Magic Flute cottage in his park at Eferding, Upper Austria. However, the Mozart Foundation succeeded in obtaining it as a present, though unfurnished. It was brought from Vienna to Salzburg and

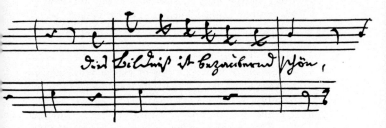

for a time it was put up in the Zwerglgarten. But this place proved unsuitable. It was dismantled again and finally set up on the Kapuzinerberg near the monastery. A silver-bearded old war veteran undertook to care for it. In his touching devotion he conveyed to the smiling and surprised visitor his own version of history.

However, watchman as well as sanctuary did not withstand the impact of time. In 1948, the little house threatened to collapse in spite of all protective measures. Therefore the "International Foundation Mozarteum" decided to dismantle it completely and subject it to a thorough scientific process of preservation. In the summer of 1950 it was set up once more, this time in the Bastiongarten of the Mozarteum.

CATALOGUE OF OBJECTS
DISPLAYED IN MOZART'S BIRTHPLACE
VESTIBULE

1. Oil-painting of Johann Lorenz Hagenauer (1712 to 1799), merchant, owner of the house in which the Mozart family lived, and friend of Leopold Mozart. Copy of the original portrait on the Hagenauer grave stone in the Churchyard of St. Peter.
2. Maria Theresia Hagenauer (1717—1800), wife of the above. Oil.
3. Maria Theresia Hagenauer. Oil-painting.
4. Ostensible Mozart as a boy of eleven years at the piano. Oil-painting by Thaddäus Helbling, done in Salzburg between 1766 and 1777.
5. Leopold Mozart, W. A. Mozart's father. Oil on wood by an unknown Salzburg painter, about 1780.

LIVING ROOM I

6. Leopold Mozart with his two children in Paris. Engraving by J. B. Delafosse (1764) from a water color by L. C. de Carmontelle. Original in the Chantilly Museum.
7. Leopold Mozart, father of Mozart. Oil on copper by an unknown painter, about 1780.

Showcase 1

8. Leopold Mozart "Essay on a complete Violin Course, Augsburg, 1756". The work was very widely used in Mozart's time and after.
9. Two cards, painted by Leopold Mozart.
10. Leopold Mozart's prayer book.
11. Shooting pictures, silk embroidery on parchment. From Leopold Mozart's possessions.

Showcase 2

12. Leopold Mozart, Mozart's father, contemporary pencil sketch.
13. Shrove Tuesday, composition by Leopold Mozart for the organ in the Fortress Hohensalzburg ("Salzburg Bull").

14. Letter from Leopold Mozart to his wife, March 13, 1770, from Milan with a post-script by W. A. Mozart. Autograph in possession of the Foundation.

Showcase 3

15. Mozart's first violin, inscribed by the manufacturer, Andreas Ferdinand Mayer, in Salzburg, 1746.

Showcase 4

16. 17. & 18. Sonates pour le Clavecin, 3 volumes first printed compositions of W. A. Mozart, published in Paris and London.

19. Gold ring, made in the form of a flower vase from emeralds, diamonds, rubies, and a small turquoise. Present of the Prince Bishop of Augsburg on the occasion of a concert by ten-year-old Mozart in 1766.

20. English plaster in envelope, brought by Mozart from England in 1765.

21. First notebook of Mozart's sister, dated 1759, with the first attempts at composition by the six-year-old Mozart in 1762. Autograph in possession of the Foundation.

22. Diary of Nannerl Mozart from the trip, 1763—1766.

Above showcase 4

23. Mozart with diamond ring. Oil by an unknown painter, apparently from Salzburg, about 1773.

Showcase 5

24. Diploma of the Accademia Filarmonica in Bologna, October 10, 1770, certifying Mozart's admission as a member of the Academy after a test composition at the age of 14.

25. Mozart's workbook, counterpoint studies. Autograph in possession of the Foundation.

26. Antiphonal "Quaerite primum regnum Dei". Composition in Mozart's own hand-writing from his test composition for the Accademia Filarmonica in Bologna.

27. Page from the exercise book of W. A. Mozart. Autograph in possession of the Foundation.
28. Johann Josef Fux: "Gradus ad Parnassum", Vienna 1725, with Leopold Mozart's bookplate.

Above showcase 6

29. Mozart with the Order of the Golden Spur. Copy of the picture in the Philharmonic Academy in Bologna.

Showcase 6

30. Kyrie in E flat major by Mozart, written about 1778 (K. 322). Autograph in possession of the Foundation.
31. Mozart. Miniature, painted in 1773. From the possession of Mozart's sister.
32. Letter from W. A. Mozart to his father, June 12, 1778, with first page by Mozart's mother.
33. Kyrie in C Major, unfinished composition by Mozart about 1780 (K. 323) with notes by Abbé Stadler. Autograph in possession of the Foundation.
34. Sinfonia Concertante, by Mozart (K. 104). Autograph in possession of the Foundation.
35. Letter of W. A. Mozart to Abbé Bullinger, Paris, July 3, 1778, in which he writes about the death of his mother.
36. First Movement of the Symphony in D Major, the so-called Paris Symphony, by Mozart (K. 297). The first six autograph pages in possession of the Foundation.

Showcase 7

37. Letter of W. A. Mozart to his sister. Vienna, February 13, 1782. Autograph in possession of the Foundation.
38. Agate tabatière. From Mozart's possession. Second tabatière.
39. Mozart's briefcase, embroidered silk.

40. Wooden relief medallion of Mozart, later reproduction of the bronze medallion made by Leonhard Posch in 1788/89, in possession of the Vienna Coin and Medallion Collection. The relief is used as a pattern for numerous Mozart representations.
41. Hanger with Mozart's hair.
42. Mother-of-pearl buttons from a court-dress coat of Mozart's.
43. Announcement of a Mozart concert on March 12, 1785, in the Imperial Royal National Theater in Vienna.
44. W. A. Mozart, sketch for a piano concerto (K. 414) with arithmetic problems.
45. Mozart's hair.
46. Ivory relief of Mozart.
47. Mozart's notice of appointment as Chamber Musician in Vienna, December 7, 1787.
48. Ticket to a Mozart-series concert in the Augarten in Vienna.
49. Mozart's hair.
50. Letter of W. A. Mozart to his father from Vienna, May 9, 1781. Autograph in possession of the Foundation.

Showcase 8
51. Floor plan of Mozart's flat on the first floor of the house on Rauhensteingasse in Vienna, drawn by J. P. Lyser, September 16, 1847.
52. The room in which Mozart died in the house on Rauhensteingasse, drawn by J. P. Lyser.
53. Andante in F Major for organ by Mozart, 1791, (K. 616). Autograph in possession of the Foundation.
54. Mother-of-pearl box with ivory writing pad from Mozart's effects.
55. Theater bill for "The Magic Flute" from the first performance in the Theater auf der Wieden in Vienna on September 30, 1791.

56. "Mozart with the Bird's Nest", oil-painting of Mozart at eight years, possibly done by Johann Zoffany in London 1764/65.
57. Mozart. Oil-painting, copy of Saverio dalla Rosa's oil-painting by L. Bode, 1858.

LIVING ROOM II
(probably the room in which Mozart was born)

58. Anna Maria Mozart, born Pertl, Mozart's mother (1720—1778). Oil by an unknown painter, about 1775.
59. Mozart's clavichord, with a range of five octaves, double stringing, built about 1760.
60. Marianne Mozart, Mozart's sister, in court dress.
61. The Mozart Family, oil by Johann Nep. de la Croce, painted in Salzburg 1780/81. The head of Mozart's mother, then dead (copied from the picture No. 58), appears as a picture hanging on the wall. (Now in the residence of the Mozart family.)
62. Mozart as a boy of six in court dress.
63. Mozart's piano, Hammerflügel with Viennese action, five-octave range, knee pedal, built about 1780 by Anton Walter in Vienna.
64. Coloured print after the painting by Saverio dalla Rosa (January 1770).
65. Mozart at the piano. Unfinished oil by Josef Lange, Court Actor and Painter, Mozart's brother-in-law, done in Vienna at the beginning of 1789.
66. Leopold Mozart. Oil-painting.

LIVING ROOM III
(probably Leopold Mozart's study)

67. Marianne Mozart (1751—1829), Mozart's sister, Freifrau Berchtold zu Sonnenburg by marriage. Oil by an unknown painter, about 1785.
68. Carl Mozart (1784—1858), the elder son of W. A. Mozart. Oil by an unknown Italian painter, about 1840. Carl Mozart lived as an official in Milan.

Showcase 1

69. Josef Haydn, engraving by J. F. Mansfeld.
70. W. A. Mozart, engraving by J. F. Mansfeld.
71. Johann Michael Haydn, silhouette.
72. Prayer book from the possessions of Sophie Haibel.
73. Mozart Medal by Voigt, 1791.
74. W. A. Mozart, bronze relief after L. Posch.
75. W. A. Mozart, medal by Bearend, 1786.
76. Pearl bag from the possessions of Sophie Haibel.

Above showcase 1

77. Carl and W. A. Mozart, Jr., Mozart's sons. Oil by the Danish painter, Hans Hansen, done in Vienna, about 1798. Mozart's other four children died either at birth or in their early years. Mozart's two surviving sons remained unmarried.

Showcase 2

78. Josef Lange, Mozart's brother-in-law. Engraving.
79. Constanze Mozart. Later Lithograph from a drawing, done at the beginning of 1789.
80. Josepha Mayer (1758—1819), widowed of Hofer, Constanze Mozart's oldest sister. Silhouette.
81. W. A. Mozart, ivory relief, unknown.
82. Constanze von Nissen, Mozart's widow. Miniature by Thomas Spitzer, Salzburg, 1826.
83. Marie Cäcilie Weber, born Stamm, Mozart's mother-in-law. Silhouette.
84. Hand-bag, made by Constanze von Nissen.
85. Georg Nikolaus von Nissen, Constanze Mozart's second husband. Miniature by Thomas Spitzer in Salzburg, 1826.
86. Obituary notice of the death of Constanze von Nissen Mozart, distributed by her sister, Sophie Haibel.
87. Autograph by Carl Mozart, W. A. Mozart's elder son, September 21, 1856.

88. Gold cross with almandins and flower ornamentations in enamel on the reverse side. From the possessions of Mozart's sister.
89. Handwritten visiting card of Mozart's sister.
90. Gold ring with enamel. From the possessions of Mozart's sister.
91. Constanze von Nissen's prayer book.
92. P. Dagobert Stamm, Constanze Mozart's uncle. Silhouette.

Above Showcase 2

93. Wolfgang Amadé Mozart, Jr. (1791—1844), Mozart's younger son, in his thirty-fourth year. Oil-painting by Karl Schweikart, 1825. W. A. Mozart, Jr., inherited musical talent from his father and was a musician by profession.

Showcase 3

94. "Life story of the Imperial Royal Orchestra Master W. A. Mozart" by Franz Xaver Niemetschek, Prague 1808.
95. "Biography of W. A. Mozart" by Georg Nikolaus von Nissen, Leipzig, 1828. Breitkopf & Härtel.
96. W. A. Mozart and his sister, miniature.
97. Letter from Constanze Mozart to her son Carl, Vienna, May 7, 1810, regarding Mozart's piano. Autograph in possession of the Foundation.
98. Lilli Lehmann Medal by Arnold Hartig.
99. Magic Flute Medal.
100. Mozart Medal, 1856.
101. Mozart Schilling from the Mozart Anniversary Year, 1931.
102. Mozart Medal by Arnold Hartig.
103. Miniature reproduction of the corner stone of the present Mozarteum.

On the walls

104. Constanze Mozart (1763—1842), Mozart's widow. Oil-painting by Hans Hansen, 1802. Constanze Mozart was at the time widowed for eleven years.

105. Georg Nikolaus von Nissen (1761—1826), Danish State councillor, Constanze Mozart's second husband. Oil-painting by Ferdinand Jagemann from Weimar, 1809, done in Vienna. Nissen, one of the first biographers of Mozart, married Constanze Mozart in 1809.

106. Baroque cupboard, containing the first collected edition of Mozart's work, published by Breitkopf & Härtel, Leipzig 1876—1883.

107. Oil-painting of Ludwig Ritter von Köchel, author of the Köchel Catalogue.

108. Maria Anna Thekla Mozart (1758—1841), Mozart's cousin, "das Bäsle". Pencil drawing, done in Augsburg, 1777/78.

109. Johann Baptist Reichsfreiherr von Berchtold zu Sonnenburg (1736—1801), Prince-archepiscopal Advisor and Representative in St. Gilgen, Marianne Mozart's husband. Marianne married her husband, who was a widower, in 1784. Oil by an unknown painter about 1785.

110. Marianne Mozart, Mozart's sister. Copy of an Oil-painting found in a private collection in Vienna.

THE KITCHEN

of the Mozart family, with an open hearth and furnished after the fashion of Mozart's time.